Saxophone

48 Studies for Alto Saxophone in E♭, Op. 31

CD contains MP3
audio and PDF™ files

By Franz Wilhelm Ferling
Edited by Daniel Schmidt
Piano Accompaniments by John Walker

CD Credits

Recorded at the Performing Arts Center on the South Dakota State University campus
Composer and Pianist: John Walker
Recording engineer: Joseph Firman
Recording assistants: Tyrone Gross and Jacob Schuring

Acknowledgements

Thanks to the South Dakota State University administration for use of the recording facility.

CARL FISCHER®

WF80

ISBN 978-0-8258-7301-0

Table of Contents

Note about the MP3 tracks:

Each Study corresponds to either 1 or 2 MP3 files on the included CD. The faster pieces have a second track with piano accompaniment at a rehearsal tempo to assist in the preparation of the piece. The MP3 files are named and tagged according to Study numbers with either "Rehearsal Tempo" or "Performance Tempo" appended.

Editorial Notes

The Ferling etudes have long been a staple of oboists and saxophonists alike. These exercises create fluency in articulation, phrasing, evenness of tone and line, ornamentation, and overall musical sophistication. All of the odd-numbered etudes feature aspects of slow, lyrical playing, while all of the even-numbered etudes feature speedy, technical exercise that will enhance facility and articulation. A few suggestions for the preparation of these two very different styles of musical performance are given below.

Lyrical Etudes

Of course, the lyrical etude is slower in nature and should enhance your phrasing and musical abilities, emphasizing the aspects of warmth, grace, elegance, beauty, and refinement in your performance. Give special attention to the note values within the etude; often with such etudes, players will ignore rests and full values on the longer tones found throughout the etude. Believe it or not, pulse is important, also. Do not rush these etudes. Rehearse the slower etude with a metronome—tempo and style marking are provided for each—to make sure that you are counting through the long tones and that you are not rushing the tempo. While it is desirable that you may wish to employ a sense of *rubato* (literally, this means "to rob," from the Italian word, *rubare*), *cantabile* (in a singing style), or other rhapsodic elements in your performance, make sure that you have a clear understanding of the underlying tempo and note rhythms first. Pay particular attention to breath marks; you may even have to incorporate your own additional phrase marks. In the preparation of solo repertoire, it is imperative that breath marks are placed to facilitate the natural breaks within larger phrase structures, and not occur randomly with little musical purpose. This is one of the most difficult assignments that the wind musician can execute, and the success of this often determines the overall success of the etude. In fact, the phrase marks that are present throughout these etudes constitute musical punctuation, and should be regarded as musical lifts, as they are setting off a specific separation of phrases as dictated by the music.

Another stumbling block may be that performers often ignore intonation, as they focus on other aspects during the performance of etudes and repertoire. Take the first note of each phrase and play this tone, in the dynamic as specified with the proper articulation, against a tuner. Remember what was necessary to place this tone in tune. Do the same exercise with the last note of the phrase. Then play the whole phrase and check the pitch on the last tone. Perhaps you could find the climax of the phrase. Then play the phrase, and sustain the tone that is the climax; check it against the tuner (also, how does the tone sound: is this a desirable tone for this note in the phrase?). Do the same exercise with the lowest note of the phrase, the highest note of the phrase, or maybe the longest note of the phrase.

All of these exercises will help you become more aware of the importance of the lyrical etude and repertoire, as these are the very concepts that constitute *musical awareness*. These etudes will also help increase your musical experience as well, as they begin to point you in the direction of true artistry. Keep in mind that *lyrical* means *songlike; characterized by emotion, subjectivity, and imagination.*

Technical Etudes

The technical etude should help to develop the performer's ability to play smoothly and evenly throughout the range of the instrument. Simply playing the tones at the prescribed tempo is not enough, however. The performer must demonstrate musicianship that transcends the mere execution of the right tones and correct articulations. The player must have an excellent idea of the overall shape of the etude: where the musical peaks and valleys are located, how dynamic contrasts fit into the shape, and the significance of the variety of articulation (or lack thereof). Without these considerations, the technical etude serves little purpose.

The process in which the technical etude is prepared is very similar to that of the lyrical etude, in fact. The same approach with initial note values is necessary. Give special attention to the note values within the etude; often with such etudes, performers will ignore rests and full values on the longer tones found throughout the etude. Do not rush the learning process for these etudes. Rehearse the technical etude with a metronome—an ultimate tempo marking is provided for each, but begin much more slowly—to make sure that you are counting through the long tones and that you are not rushing the tempo. When beginning the technical etude, use the same approach that you utilize during the preparation of scale and arpeggio patterns. In fact, if the preparation of scales and arpeggio patterns is proper, this will facilitate the preparation of the technical etude, as these etudes often comprise such patterns.

Set the metronome to a slow and reasonable marking, and begin to play the etude. If you have picked a speed that is too slow, then you will simply experience great success in its preparation. After you have mastered this tempo—*but only after you have mastered this tempo*—increase the speed of the metronome by one click (four beats per minute). Remember: increase the speed *only* when you have mastered the previous tempo. It is much easier to learn these patterns from scratch, as opposed to "re-learning" them, rife with wrong fingerings, articulations, unevenness, and a myriad of other bad habits. While this process may seem slow and tedious, this is the shortest distance between two points, in fact. If you skip the mastery of each step to simply crank up the tempo on the metronome, then the product of your practice will be an uneven, "dirty" etude, and you are simply wasting your time. For this reason, it is recommended that you do not write in breath marks until the tempo is close to the suggested tempo, as breath marks may change with the increase of speed. In addition, try to make sure that the breath marks fit the overall phrase structure, and are not placed solely for the purpose of facilitating your breath. Sometimes this may not be possible in a long run of tones, and it is permissible to leave a tone out, as long as the pulse is not interrupted. Not only will a properly prepared Ferling technical etude demonstrate great instrumental technique, or *flash,* but it will also demonstrate the performer's understanding of the importance of diligence and work ethic, and demonstrate the performer's ability to practice in a methodical, structured manner.

Keep in mind that there are style markings for these technical exercises as well as metronome markings, giving further guidance for a sophisticated musical interpretation of these etudes.

Special thanks should go out to my good friend and oboist Nancy Clauter for her careful suggestions on articulations and phrasing, as well as her biography on Ferling, included in this book. John Walker's diligent work on the piano accompaniment brings this new experience to life. Enjoy!

—Daniel Schmidt

About Franz Wilhelm Ferling

Franz Wilhelm Ferling was a German performer, composer, and teacher. He was born on September 20, 1796 (five years after Mozart died) in Hallerbstadt, and he died in Brunswick (*Braunschweig*) on December 18, 1874. He spent most of his professional career (1814–1859) in service to the Brunswick Duchy, which is in Lower Saxony, now Northwestern Germany. During Ferling's time there, it was part of the territory of Wolfenbüttel, with Brunswick as its capital. In 1815, at the Congress of Vienna, the first year of Ferling's employment, this area of Lower Saxony gained sovereignty as a state and was declared an independent country under the name "Duchy of Brunswick."

This area, though culturally rich since as far back as the 1300s, was undergoing great turmoil during Ferling's early time of employment. Ferling would have worked under two very different administrations: Charles II from 1815–1830—at the end of his reign, his palace at Brunswick was completely destroyed by the 1830 July Revolution—and William VIII from 1839–1884. William VIII had a strained relationship with Prussia, which annexed Hanover in 1866, but left the Duchy of Brunswick as independent, until it was annexed into the German Empire in 1871 (three years before Ferling's death).

Since Ferling was both a clarinetist and an oboist, his first assignment included playing clarinet in the military for a few years before attaining Principal Oboe of the Brunswick Court Theater where he stayed until 1859, when he retired. As a teacher, he would have been very aware of a diverse group of musical genres, which included the operas of Bellini, Donizetti, Rossini and Meyerbeer; German opera, however, was not the norm until the great German composer Richard Wagner returned from his musical defection to Paris after 1842. Other genres and influences would have included the piano music of Brahms, Liszt, Schumann, and Chopin with their lush melodic structures and folk-dance idioms, as well as the symphonic works of the great Germanic traditions of Beethoven. All of these influences, plus the glory days of the Paris Conservatoire, had to play a role in the compositional creativity of the oboist/teacher.

Ferling wrote the *48 Studies for Oboe*, Op. 31 in 1840. He set the collection up into two sets of opposing tempi, each paired in the same major key; these were then followed by another pair of opposing tempi, paired in the relative minor key. The proceeding keys were related by the circle of fifths, with sharp keys being followed by flat ones. The main melodic influences were slow movement sonata/concerto style (including *cadenzi* moments), Romantic elaboration of dance styles, and Italian and French opera. The harmonic structure is somewhat simple, and the musical forms are the well-known forms, such as binary and trio/da capo. The range, breath control and expressive style, coupled with articulation clarity, are the most delicate and difficult combinations to achieve. Clearly, Ferling was a master at playing the oboe and saw to it that his students (and one of his two sons, who also played the oboe) would be masters of its wily temperament as well.

—Nancy Clauter

About Daniel Schmidt

Dr. Daniel J. Schmidt is Director of Bands and Associate Professor of Music at Northern Arizona University in Flagstaff, Arizona. Prior to this appointment he was director of bands and professor of saxophone and double reeds at Mars Hill College in North Carolina. College ensembles under his direction have received international reputations, touring Europe, performing at various conventions, including the CBDNA Regional Conventions in 2002 and 2006, and making promotional recordings for Warner Bros. Music and Carl Fischer Music. Prior to Dr. Schmidt's appointment at MHC, he was the associate director of bands at Syracuse University, directing the 230-piece "Pride of the Orange" marching band and various concert and pep bands. Dr. Schmidt received the Bachelor of Music Education degree from the Florida State University and was appointed director of bands at Hudson High School in Pasco County, Florida, in 1987. He is the first person to receive the Master of Music in wind conducting from the University of North Texas while emphasizing saxophone performance and musicology (1993). Dr. Schmidt is also the first person to receive the Doctorate of Musical Arts in wind conducting from the University of Kentucky (2000). Dr. Schmidt was the recipient of a Fulbright Award to Australia in 1993, but refused this opportunity to join the Syracuse University faculty. He has served as clinician and adjudicator throughout the country. He has enjoyed a relationship with Carl Fischer Music of New York for several years. Projects have included acting as the coordinating editor for the series of band scores entitled *Percy Grainger: The Critical Edition*. He is the author of *My First Klosé, My First Wagner, My First Universal Method, My First Barrett*, and *My First Weissenborn*, five intermediate lesson workbooks for woodwinds, and is the co-author of *Protocol: A Guide to the Collegiate Audition* Process for flute, clarinet, saxophone, trumpet, trombone, tuba, violin, cello, and bass. He is the conductor of the Trade Winds, a professional ensemble that does promotional recordings of new music for Carl Fischer, Wingert-Jones, and Play-n-Time Music since 2002. He has been a clinician for the UMKC Conservatory of Music's *Wind Band Teaching Symposium* in the summers since 2007. Dr. Schmidt is also a performing artist for the Yamaha Corporation of America and is the Arizona State Chair for the College Band Directors National Association as well as Vice-President for the Western Region.

About John Walker

John Walker holds a Doctor of Musical Arts degree from the University of Colorado at Boulder, Master of Music from the San Francisco Conservatory of Music, and Bachelor of Music from the University of California at Santa Barbara. He studied piano pedagogy at the New School for Music Study under Frances Clark and Louise Goss.

Dr. Walker is Professor of Music and Director of Keyboard Studies at South Dakota State University, and Principal Keyboard for the South Dakota Symphony Orchestra. His performances include solo appearances with the South Dakota Symphony and Chamber Orchestra, and has performed solo and chamber music in Italy, Switzerland, Slovenia and throughout the American midwest.

John Walker is the first Patricia Pierce Distinguished Artist in Residence at SDSU, and is a recipient of of the College of Arts & Sciences Distinguished Performer Award and the F. O. Butler Award for Faculty Excellence in Creative Activity.

Notes on Performing with the MP3 Accompaniments

These accompaniments may be used for practice to add rhythmic interest, contrapuntal depth, and harmonic realization to what is already implied in the solo studies, as well as for contests, auditions, or recital performances. The accompaniments should provide a satisfying complement to the studies, and turn these beautiful solo pieces into beautiful accompanied recital pieces. I hope you enjoy them.

There are metronome clicks before each piece. For fast tempos, the beat is given; for slower tempos, the division of the beat is usually given. Two of the pieces have composed introductions instead of clicks. Some pieces have cadenza or *ad lib.* material, for which space is given on the recording. When pieces begin with upbeats, those are included in the metronome clicks below, with space allowed for the upbeat notes.

The following are metronome clicks and specific notes for each study.

Study No. 1. 4 clicks

Study No. 2. 4 clicks. In m. 10 the piano fills in the two beats of rest with material which anticipates (is the same as) the oboe entrance on the downbeat of the following measure. This creates a brief canon effect begun by the piano.

Study No. 3. 6 clicks

Study No. 4. 4 clicks. Count four beats for the grand pause.

Study No. 5. 4 clicks

Study No. 6. 4 clicks

Study No. 7. 6 clicks + 2 spaces

Study No. 8. 4 clicks. In m. 9 the piano imitates the oboe part two beats later to create a brief canon effect begun by the oboe. Measure 24 has four beats of piano trills.

Study No. 9. 6 clicks

Study No. 10. 4 bars of introduction (no clicks)

Study No. 11. 6 clicks

Study No. 12. 4 clicks

Study No. 13. 3 clicks

Study No. 14. 4 clicks

Study No. 15. 4 clicks

Study No. 16. 6 clicks

Study No. 17. 4 clicks. At the end of the cadenza, four clicks are given for re-entry at the following measure.

Study No. 18. 4 clicks

Study No. 19. 4 clicks

Study No. 20. 4 clicks

Study No. 21. 4 clicks. At m. 8, second beat, the piano plays the same dotted-rhythm melody that the oboe plays on the fourth beat, thereby creating a short canon begun by the piano.

Study No. 22. 4 clicks. Count four beats for the grand pause at m. 16.

Study No. 23. 3 clicks

Study No. 24. 2 measures of introduction (no clicks)

Study No. 25. 4 clicks

Study No. 26. 3 clicks. The piano right hand is always on the beat; the left hand emphasizes the offbeats.

Study No. 27. 6 clicks

Study No. 28. 4 clicks. The piano fills in the grand pause at m. 16. The following downbeat should be easy to hear.

Study No. 29. 4 clicks. At m. 6 (*ad lib.*), the piano plays a chord on the fermata, then another chord on the last four eighth notes.

Study No. 30. 4 clicks

Study No. 31. 6 clicks

Study No. 32. 4 clicks

Study No. 33. 4 clicks. After the *ad libitum* measure (m. 15), the piano plays on the downbeat of m. 16.

Study No. 34. 4 clicks

Study No. 35. 6 clicks

Study No. 36. 4 clicks. The piano fills in the grand pause at m. 26 with three quarter notes and a fermata.

Study No. 37. 4 clicks

Study No. 38. 4 clicks

Study No. 39. 6 clicks. The piano part is quite chromatic.

Study No. 40. 4 clicks. Apologies to Ludwig. Count two measures rest for the grand pause at m. 55.

Study No. 41. 4 clicks

Study No. 42. 4 clicks

Study No. 43. 3 clicks + 1 space

Study No. 44. 4 clicks

Study No. 45. 3 clicks

Study No. 46. 7 clicks + 1 space

Study No. 47. 4 clicks

Study No. 48. 4 clicks. At the fermata (m. 54) the piano plays briefly *ad libitum* with a short fermata.

—John Walker

48 Studies for Saxophone in E♭, Op. 31

FRANZ WILHELM FERLING
(1796–1874)
Edited by Daniel Schmidt

Study No. 1

Study No. 2

Study No. 3

Study No. 4

12

Study No. 5

Andante cantabile ♪ = 80

Study No. 6

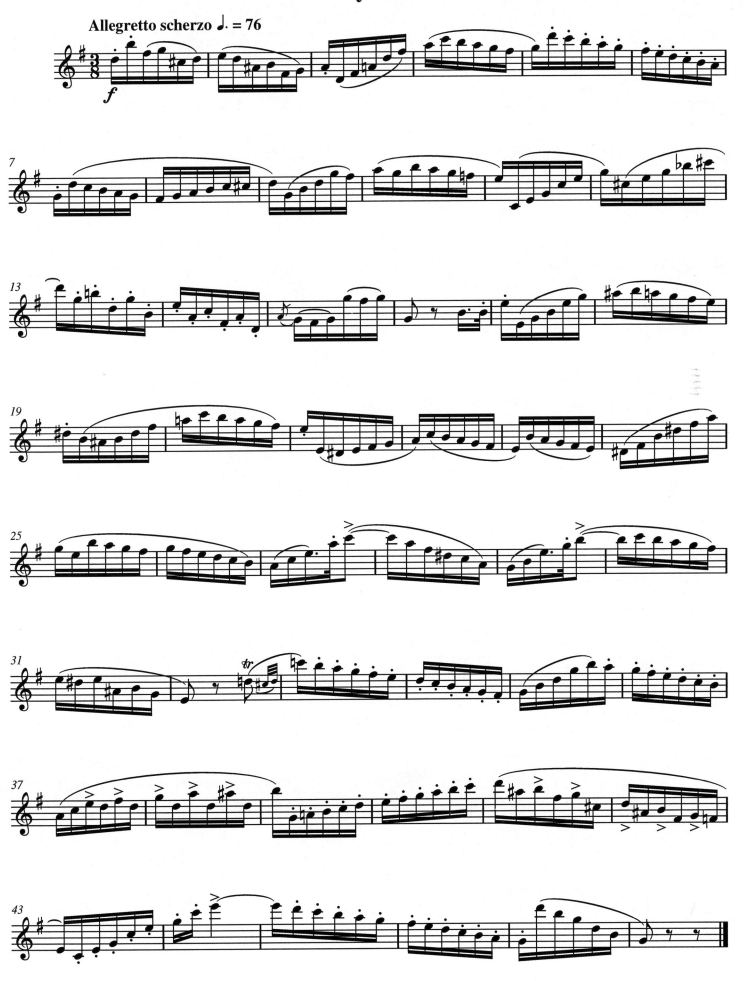

Study No. 7

Study No. 8

Allegro moderato con fuoco ♩ = 120

Study No. 9

Adagio con espressione ♪ = 88

Study No. 10

Study No. 11

Study No. 12

Study No. 13

Study No. 14

Study No. 15

Study No. 16

Study No. 17

Study No. 18

Study No. 19

WF80

Study No. 20

Study No. 21

Study No. 22

Study No. 23

Study No. 24

Study No. 25

Study No. 26

Study No. 27

Study No. 28

Study No. 29

Andante amabile ♪ = 88

Study No. 30

Allegro poco moderato ♩ = 116

Study No. 31

Study No. 32

Study No. 33

Study No. 34

42

Study No. 35

Study No. 36

Study No. 37

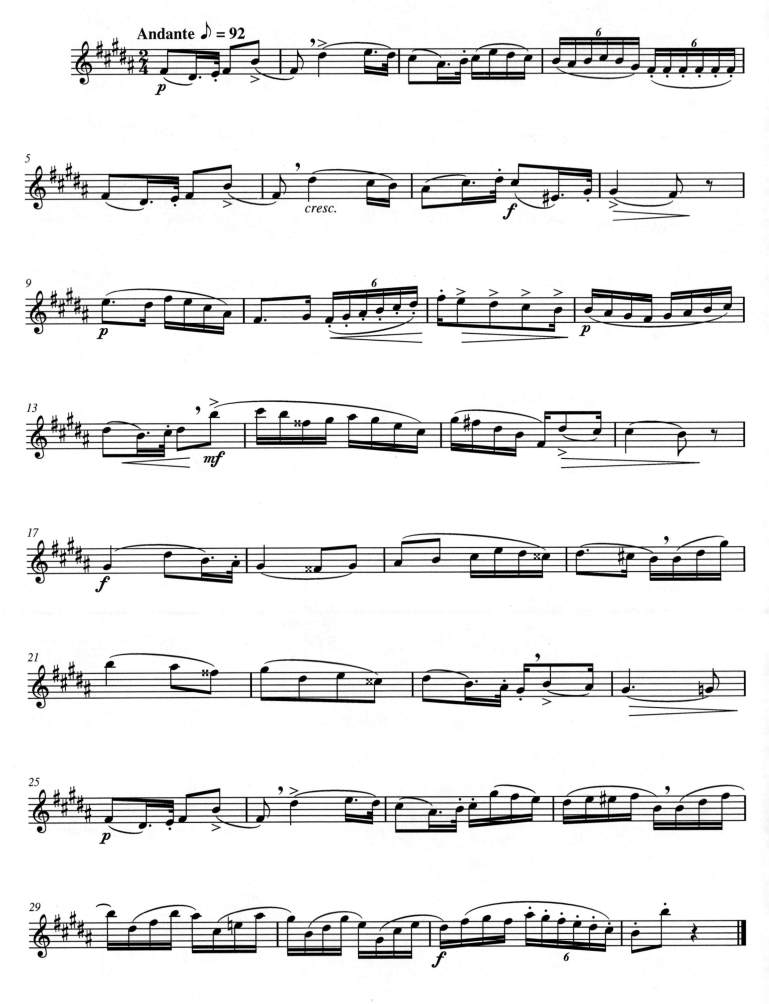

Study No. 38

Study No. 39

Study No. 40

Study No. 41

Study No. 42

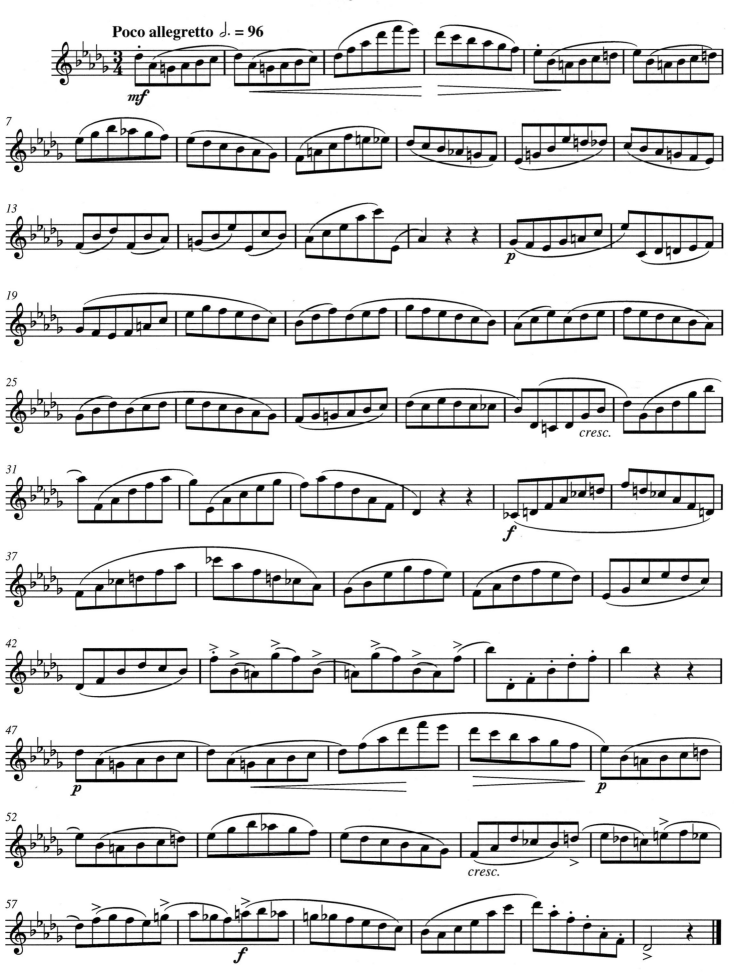

Study No. 43

Study No. 44

Study No. 45

Study No. 46

Study No. 47

Study No. 48

About John Walker

John Walker holds a Doctor of Musical Arts degree from the University of Colorado at Boulder, Master of Music from the San Francisco Conservatory of Music, and Bachelor of Music from the University of California at Santa Barbara. He studied piano pedagogy at the New School for Music Study under Frances Clark and Louise Goss.

Dr. Walker is Professor of Music and Director of Keyboard Studies at South Dakota State University, and Principal Keyboard for the South Dakota Symphony Orchestra. His performances include solo appearances with the South Dakota Symphony and Chamber Orchestra, and has performed solo and chamber music in Italy, Switzerland, Slovenia and throughout the American midwest.

John Walker is the first Patricia Pierce Distinguished Artist in Residence at SDSU, and is a recipient of of the College of Arts & Sciences Distinguished Performer Award and the F. O. Butler Award for Faculty Excellence in Creative Activity.